First published 2008 AD
This edition © Wooden Books Ltd 2008 AD

Published by Wooden Books Ltd.
8A Market Place, Glastonbury, Somerset

British Library Cataloguing in Publication Data
Gillam, F.
Poisonous Plants in Great Britain

A CIP catalogue record for this book is
available from the British Library

ISBN 978 1 904263 87 6

Recycled paper throughout.
All rights reserved.
For permission to reproduce any part of this
useful book please contact the publishers.

Printed and bound in England by
The Cromwell Press, Trowbridge, Wiltshire.
100% recycled papers made specially for
Wooden Books by by Paperback.

POISONOUS
PLANTS
IN GREAT BRITAIN

Frederick Gillam

For Jack

This book is not a field guide and if you want to learn to identify flora and fungi in the wild, you will need to obtain the relevant field guides. My personal preference for flowering plants is "The Wildflower Key" by Francis Rose. For fungi I use Roger Phillips' "Mushrooms and other Fungi of Great Britain and Europe" which is bulky, but great for its photographs.

Thanks go to Lydia Maskell for stoic patience and support, George and Patricia Dorothy Gillam for tales of Queen Anne's Lace and lessons in tending the garden, to Mike Slater for enthusiasm and encouragement, and to the kingdom of nature, of which we are each a part, for the materials and the muse.

The illustrations are reworked from antiquarian botanical woodcuts, copperplate engravings and lithographs by famous artists. The artists are James Sowerby ('English Botany' 1790-1813 and 'Medical Botany' 1790-94), Walther Müller ('Flora von Deutschland, Elizabeth Johns ('Flowers of the Field' 1889 ed.), Ostereich und der Schweiz' 1885 and 'Medizinal Pflanzen' 1883-87), Mordecai Cubitt Cooke ('Edible and Poisonous Mushrooms' 1894), Michael/Martin Rössler ('Flora Danica' 1761-), Albin Schmalfuss ('Führer für Pilzfreunde' 1901), G. Bresadola ('i Funghi Mangerecci e Velenosi' 1906). Fly agaric illustration by Scottish engraver William Miller ('Scottish Cryptogamic Flora' 1823-28). Mandrake by Matthäeus Merian ('Viridarium Reformatum' 1719). Frontispiece from the Tacuinum Sanitati of Vienna, Circa 1400. Illustration facing Introduction by Bernard Zuber (La Vie Execrable de Guillemete Babin, Sorciere 1926)'. Title page woodcut from Christian Egenolff ('Herbarum, Arborum, Fruticum, Frumentorum ac Leguminem' 1546). Hercules capturing Kerberos (p.3) by Sebald Beham ('The Labours of Hercules' 1545).

CONTENTS

INTRODUCTION

None should venture out into field or forest to gather food or remedies without some knowledge of the plants and fungi that may cause harm, or even prove deadly, if consumed. At 14 years of age I foolishly collected and ingested a very poisonous *inocybe* mushroom, and as a consequence developed a healthy interest and respect for the poisonous plants and fungi.

This little book contains plenty to fascinate and inform young and old alike. There are notes on appearance, symptoms of poisoning, antidotes and anecdotes. Many of the most poisonous species are illustrated, using antique prints from some of the greatest botanical artists to have lived. However, this book is not a comprehensive guide, for which a far larger volume would be required, neither is it intended to be a substitute for a reliable field guide to the identification of species, of which there are many available.

The information in this book is designed to help the naturalist, wild-food collector, folklorist, parent or livestock owner to carry out their respective tasks in an informed way. Anecdotes are provided for your information and entertainment only, and are not intended to promote experimentation with ANY of the plants and fungi listed. To any who would be so tempted, I implore you to reflect upon these words from a memorial stone;

"As I Was, So Are Thee
As I Am, So Wilt Thou Bee"

St. Nicholas Church, Bromham, Wiltshire

A FEW WISE WORDS
how to use this book

"All things are poison and nothing is without poison,
only the dose permits something not to be poisonous"

Paracelsus, alchemist and physician, 1493 - 1591

FIRST OF ALL, AND MOST IMPORTANTLY, ALWAYS REMEMBER THAT POISONS ARE POISONOUS. TAKE CARE WHEN DEALING WITH EVERYTHING ABOUT THEM. READ THE BOOKS RECOMMENDED ON PAGE IV.

SECONDLY, IF YOU GO OUT COLLECTING, ALWAYS RETAIN SOME SPECIMENS FOR IDENTIFICATION. WHEN YOU GET HOME, YOU CAN MAKE USE OF THE INTERNET, OR A TEXTUAL KEY LIKE 'THE BRITISH EXCURSION FLORA'. SHOW THEM TO AN EXPERT AT YOUR LOCAL WILDLIFE TRUST OR BIOLOGICAL RECORDS OFFICE. KEEP UNIDENTIFIED SPECIMENS SEPARATE FROM ANY THAT YOU ARE COLLECTING FOR FOOD; SOMETIMES EVEN TINY AMOUNTS CAN BE POISONOUS.

THIRDLY, BOOK YOURSELF ONTO SOME FUNGUS FORAYS WITH A LOCAL MUSHROOM EXPERT. THE ADVICE AND CONNECTIONS YOU MAKE WILL STAND YOU IN GOOD STEAD, AND THE EXPERIENCE COULD BE SOMETHING THAT YOU CHERISH.

FINALLY, IF YOU THINK THAT SOMEBODY HAS BEEN POISONED, SEEK MEDICAL ATTENTION IMMEDIATELY. DO NOT HESITATE. IF POSSIBLE, TAKE A SAMPLE OF THE OFFENDING MATERIAL WITH YOU TO THE NEAREST HOSPITAL. REMEMBER, TIME IS OF THE ESSENCE, AND PROMPT ACTION SAVES LIVES.

Above: Hercules' twelfth labour, the subjugation of Kerberos, guardian of Hades.
Below: Socrates accepts the death penalty and ends his life by drinking hemlock.

MONKSHOOD - WOLFSBANE
Aconitum napellus

Family: *Ranunculaceae*. Synonyms: *Wolf's bane, blue rocket, auld wife's huid, helmet flower*. A garden escape in damp places, woodland edges and mountain pasture, but may be native in the West Country. From June to August the blue-mauve flowers resemble the hood of a monk's robe. This plant competes with hemlock water dropwort for the title of Europe's most dangerous plant. Wear gloves when handling, and prevent dogs, cats and children from digging nearby.

The Greeks called it *akontion* or 'dart', because it was used to tip arrows – whence also 'wolfsbane', but monkshood could have been named 'ratsbane' because it was once used to poison them. The Anglo-Saxons called it *thung* – meaning 'poison plant'. Theophrastus and Pliny derived the name from *Aconae*, its place of origin, and *napellus* means 'little turnip', alluding to the root. Hekate, goddess of witchcraft, transformed the foam issuing from Kerberos (the 3 headed hound of Diana slain by Hercules at a crossroads) into monkshood. Gerard, the 16th century herbalist wrote: *"So acrid is the poison that the juice applied to a wounded finger ... causes pains in the limbs and a sense of suffocation and syncope."*

Those affected clutch at their throat and experience the terrible sensation of ants creeping beneath the skin. The main principle is aconitine, which has been used topically for neuralgia and pain relief. The herb is an ingredient in mediaeval accounts of the witches' 'flying ointment' (other alleged ingredients included henbane, foxglove and deadly nightshade), and interestingly, both atropine (from nightshades) and digitalis (from foxglove) act as antidotes to aconitine. Once thought to remedy scorpion stings and prevent the transformation of werewolves, today it is used homeopathically for nervous excitement.

5

WHITE BRYONY
Bryonia dioica

Family: *Cucurbitaceae*. Synonyms: *English mandrake, wild vine, wild nep, tamus, Ladies' seal, tetterbury*. Found in woodlands and hedgerows throughout Britain, especially the south. A vine-like perennial producing tendrils that lie to the side of the lobed hairy leaves enabling it to climb to 3m. Small whitish inconspicuous flowers are produced from May onwards, later becoming clusters of scarlet berries. Each plant bears flowers of only one sex. The only native British member of the cucumber family, and a violent irritant poison. Important to honeybees but deadly to humans.

2000 years ago the root as 'thick as a man's thigh' was known to Dioscorides and Pliny, and Galen employed its acrid juice in epilepsy (though occasionally it acted too violently). In the scarcity that followed the French Revolution it became a nutritious food after thorough methodical preparation. The poison attacks the digestive tract, causing vomiting, watery purgation with urination, intense abdominal pain and inflammation. Historical uses include the treatment of intestinal worms, ringworm or 'tetters', dropsy and rheumatic heart, malaria and all of the 19th century infectious maladies. It relieved the pain and persistence of whooping cough and was applied externally producing localised heat to ease painful joints. Norfolk horsemen fed small quantities with corn to condition their beasts, and it was used to purge sick cattle.

In mediaeval times the root became 'English mandrake' after attaining human shape by being grown in a mould, or carved and re-buried so that the bark would scar over. A thin scallop would be cut in the crown of the root where grass seed was planted to resemble hair. Mandrakes, both genuine and 'English', fetched high prices and were used in folk magic to attract love and luck, or to heal and curse from afar (*see mandrake, page 20*).

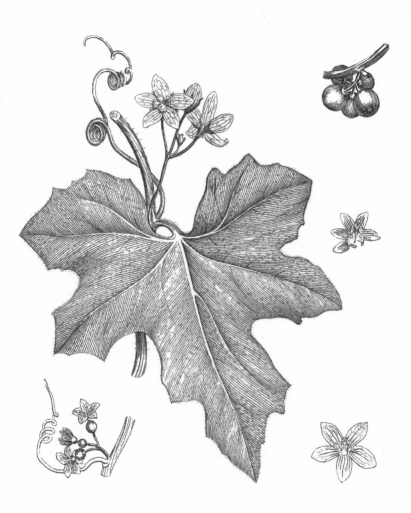

BLACK BRYONY
Tamus communis

Family: *Dioscoreaceae*. Synonyms: *Black-eye root, chilblain berry, big root*. A weak stemmed climber with very shiny heart shaped leaves, pale green flowers and red berries. The root has black bark and is actually a poisonous yam. Once in widespread use as a medicine (despite common accidental poisonings), this plant can lead to a very painful death. The acrid root was employed as an external irritant in paralysis, rheumatism and gout; stimulating circulation to promoting healing. It was used to clear gravel from the urinary tract, and is still used homeopathically for this purpose. Mrs. Grieve, in her *Modern Herbal* [1931], tells us that a tincture of the berries was used to treat unbroken chillblains, and the young shoots were prepared like asparagus and eaten by the Greeks and the Moors. It was used in the West Country to condition horses and make their coats shine, but 'Bryony served too dry, blinded horses when they blew'. 'Black eye root' refers to its former use in a poultice to remedy the discolouration of bruising.

Pliny's *Uva taminia* is thought to be this plant. Tammuz was the shepherd god of the Sumerians (the name means 'True Son'). Mythology recounts his descent into the underworld to release the goddess Inanna, and thereafter he was permitted to return to earth each year for six months at the winter solstice. Black Bryony is also the seal of the Virgin Mary at the Feast of the Nativity.

Some species of yams used as staple foods by aboriginal peoples in Africa, Asia and Australia are deadly arrow poisons. Recently, survival expert Ray Mears and archaeobotanist Gordon Hillman have been experimenting to see if our ancestors could have safely used the root of black bryony as a food, using aboriginal methods of preparation.

9

DEADLY NIGHTSHADE
Atropa belladonna

Family: *Solanaceae*. Synonyms: *Dwale, black morel* (as in morello), *great morel, devil's cherry, moonshade*. Mostly southern, favouring waste-land and scrub on chalk and lime soils. The dark purple bells tinged with green from June to September are followed by appealing shiny black fruits. The cherry like fruits can be unwittingly gathered and eaten, causing serious illness or death. Especially dangerous to children.

The task of Atropa, one of the Greek Moirae or 'three fates', was to sever the thread of life. Belladonna means 'beautiful woman', and historically the juice was applied to the eyes making them sparkle, though this was hazardous. Having a long association with witchcraft and shamanism during the middle ages, it was an attested ingredient of the salve, or 'flying ointment' that led to the perception of magical flight to a convocation of witches and spirits known as the 'sabbat'. The modern use of belladonna during the witchcraft revival of the 1960's caused the death of noted witch Robert Cochrane (1966).

Deadly nightshade contains atropine, hyoscyamine and hyoscine. Historically an external application was used to treat foul ulcers and it is used today to treat the spasmodic pain of peptic ulcers and urinary spasms. Overdose causes disorientation, hallucination, coma and death; as with many of the plants in this book – the difference between the therapeutic and toxic dosage is small. Atropine sulphate is used in eye examinations to dilate the pupil, and belladonna is widely used in homeopathy where toxicity is of no concern. Opium has been used as an antidote to atropine poisoning, and in turn atropine is an antidote to poisoning from monkshood and foxglove, and muscarine poisoning from certain fungi.

BLACK NIGHTSHADE
Solanum nigrum

Family: *Solanaceae*. Synonyms: *Petty morel, garden nightshade*. A short to medium white flowered annual of waste ground, compost heaps and hedge bottoms. Poisonous and possibly deadly under some circumstances, yet used as food in many parts of the world. Avoid eating.

A remarkable illustration of this plant is found in the oldest surviving copy of Dioscorides' *De Materia Medica* dating from 512 AD, housed in the National Library of Vienna. Theophrastus too was familiar with it, and both authors treated it as an edible plant. Dr. Woodville, in his *Medical Botany* [1794], remarked that there was much debate over its toxicity, some cases revealing severe narcotic action, with others failing to show effect. In one instance a mother, father and child ate it as a vegetable; the mother and child were taken ill but the father was not. It was used to treat internal and external ulcers and cancers. Bruised leaves were applied for pain and inflammation, and their juice used to treat ringworm and gout. The Arab physicians applied the leaves to burns and ulcers.

Mrs. Grieve tells us that peasants in Bohemia placed the herb in the cradle to promote sleep. The herb certainly has a documented sedative and narcotic action similar to bittersweet but stronger; however this action does not appear to be present reliably at all times of the year and in all regions. In some parts of the world certain strains are eaten as a green vegetable – the boiling water being first discarded. The fruits of certain varieties, including Garden Huckleberry are eaten when fully ripe in puddings, but eating the unripe fruits could certainly cause poisoning. Children are very susceptible to nightshades and should always be warned to stay clear of the berries, whether ripe or not.

13

BLACK HENBANE
Hyoscyamus niger

Family: *Solanaceae*.   Synonyms: *Jupiter's-bean*, *hog's-bean*, *deus caballinus* (C13 lit. 'horse god'), *Devil's eye*, *stinking nightshade*, *henbell* (Anglo-Saxon), *jusquiame* (French), *symphonica*. A lax-stemmed annual with lobed leaves and covered in sticky glandular hairs. Its unusual purple-veined yellow flowers with dark centres are evocative of the name 'Devil's eye'. Henbane is found in well drained sunny sites and waste ground, favouring chalk and sandy soils. Deadly and similar in effect to deadly nightshade, the roots have been mistaken for parsnips.

In classical times henbane was a local and general anaesthetic. The ancient Egyptians deadened toothache by allowing the smoke from smouldering henbane to enter the mouth and the priestesses at the Oracle of Delphi used it to assist in their prophecy. Associated with confusion and madness, it served to confound even the the dead in Hades, who were crowned with the herb making them forget their former lives as they walked beside the river Styx. Henbane was used in the witches' 'flying ointment' and was probably the inspiration for the moment in Apuleius' *The Golden Ass* [c. 170 AD] when Pamphile transformed herself into an owl. According to Gerard "oft smelling of the flowers causeth sleep". First hand accounts from the medically supervised use of henbane record deep sleep interspersed with lucid perceptions of long distance flight, and a sensation of lifting from the ground whilst walking.

The active ingredients are atropine, hyoscine and hyoscyamine. In medicine, preparations are used for spasmodic pain, toothache and asthma. Hyoscine is used as a pre-medication in anaesthesia and in travel sickness pills. Henbane causes an elevation of blood pressure and pulse. Overdose causes central nervous system paralysis, respiratory collapse and death.

15

BITTERSWEET
Solanum dulcamara

Family: *Solanaceae.* Synonyms: *Woody nightshade, felonwort, felonwood, poisonberry.* Found in woodland and scrub, hedge banks and marshes. A perennial climber reaching ten feet, with acrid smelling foliage and small blue-purple potato-like flowers with orange stamens that form clusters of oval red berries. Less toxic than the deadly nightshade, but has caused fatalities, particularly in children who sometimes mistake the ripe berries for redcurrants.

Dulce amara means 'sweet bitter' as the plant allegedly tastes bitter at first, then very sweet. *Solanum* may be derived from *solamen* meaning to comfort – perhaps linked to its effectiveness in treating leprosy. 'Felonwort' refers to the practice of using bittersweet pounded with bacon to remove felons or whitlows on the fingers but don't try this at home as toxins can be absorbed through the skin. In shepherd lore, bittersweet protected flocks from the evil eye, and a piece of the wood was hung from the neck of sheep in danger from 'overlooking' by witches.

Dioscorides, in the 1st century AD used our herb to remove spots from the skin. Later it was used for tuberculosis, rheumatism and absence of menstruation. In 1792 Woodville commented that thirty berries killed a dog in three hours, yet later trials used six times the dose and produced no effects. Overdose paralyses the central nervous system, leading to respiratory collapse and a convulsive death. Another effect is the loss of speech, which may be the source of tales of people struck dumb by a witch's curse. Today, medical herbalists use bittersweet to treat herpes, allergies, and conditions affecting the mucous membranes, the active ingredients being dulcamarine and solanine.

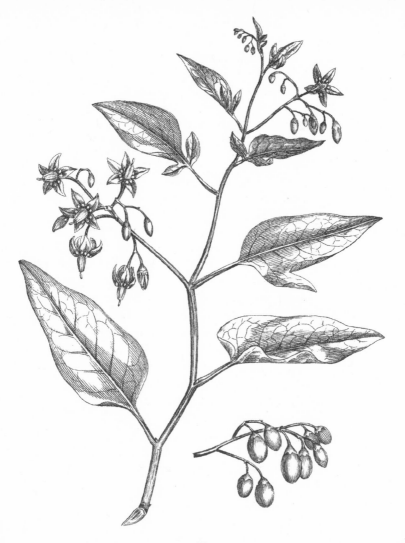

THORNAPPLE
Datura stramonium

Family: *Solanaceae*. Synonyms: *Devil's weed, stinkweed, Devil's apple, jimson weed*. A tall annual with broad, deeply-toothed leaves and large white trumpet flowers, each with five petals terminating in a point. An occasional of waste ground, although various coloured varieties are grown in gardens. Widely distributed throughout the world, together with a number of similar species. Flowering June to October. The settlers of Jamestown Virginia ate this plant and suffered madness and fatalities; hence the name jimsonweed or 'Jamestown-weed'. To inhale of the flower's scent too vigorously leaves the inhaler dazed and confused. A deadly poison.

Thornapple was a shamanic 'plant of power' in the books about Central American sorcerer Don Juan, by Carlos Castaneda. In Voudon culture a species of *datura* is used in the zombie potion administered to those who commit crimes against society. The Thugees, who robbed travellers who crossed India used 'dhat' to stupefy their male victims before sacrificing them to Kali, and the sacred 'dhat' flower is also offered to its originator, Shiva, at sacred omphali on the 13th day of the January waxing moon.

Smoking *datura* for the effective relief of asthma was once popularised in Britain by an army general who had encountered it in Hindusthan. Thornapple contains the same tropane alkaloids as deadly nightshade and henbane, and in many respects their medical and entheogenic histories are similar. However in some cases *datura* intoxication, accompanied by visions of convincing reality, can last for longer than a week and can either be profound or profoundly disturbing. Usually, as the effects abate the memories of the experience also fade. Overdose paralyses the central nervous system and leads to death.

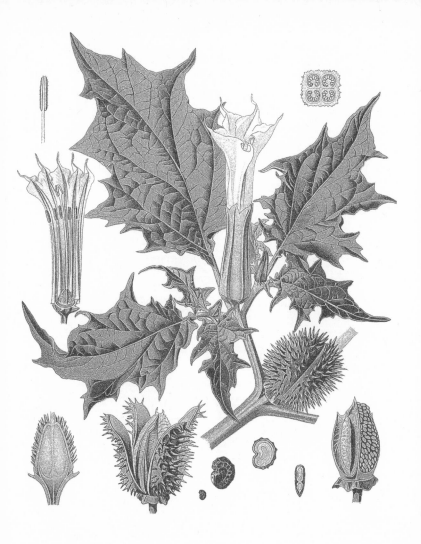

19

MANDRAKE
Mandragora officinarum

Family: *Solanaceae*. Synonyms: *Satan's apple*, *love apple*, from German; 'dragon doll', 'gallows man'. Found in Southern Europe and Asia, but important in British folklore. Deadly, though in Persia some strains had edible fruits. References to mandrake in the Old Testament illustrate its traditional association with amour:

> *"Jacob came out of the field in the evening, and Leah went out to meet him and said, you must sleep with me [tonight], for I have certainly paid your hire with my son's mandrakes. So he slept with her that night."*   Genesis 30:16.

> *"The mandrakes give forth fragrance, and over our doors are all manner of choice fruits, new and old, which I have laid up for you, O my beloved!"*
>
> Song of Solomon 7:13

In Hebrew mandrake is דודאים (dûdã'im), or 'love plant' referring to its aphrodisial qualities. In Arabic the fruit is *beid el-jinn*, or genies' eggs.

Named after draco and endowed with life-force, mandrake was placed under a bed, or over the mantle or threshold to bring conception, attract love and luck. The anthropomorphic root could house the witch's familiar or be baptised in a person's name to work magic on them for benefit or bane. It was said to grow under the gallows where the semen of hanged men fell to earth and if whosoever uprooted it should hear the plant scream they would die, so a dog was often employed to uproot it. Similar in composition to deadly nightshade, henbane and thornapple (see) it was like them used in witches' 'flying ointments', and was also used as a charm to repel evil from Anglo-Saxon times. Medically the mandrake treated pain, rheumatism, and foul ulcers, and was a general anaesthetic; the danger of it causing madness or death being well known.

21

GREEN & STINKING HELLEBORE
Helleborus viridis and foetidus

Family: *Ranunculaceae*. Synonym: *Bear's foot*. Green hellebore is a short woodland perennial with serrated leaves divided so that they resemble the fingers of a hand. A welcome sight toward the end of winter, its small green rose-like blooms are among the first to grace shady woodland banks. All Hellebores are narcotic-irritant poisons, causing vomiting, diarrhoea, severe pain, convulsions and death. However it is unlikely to be confused with anything.

Hellebores were used medicinally by the physicians of Ancient Greece and Asia Minor. In Greek mythology, hellebore saved the king of Argos' daughters from the madness inflicted by Dionysos, that caused them to run through the streets naked, screaming and crying.

Green hellebore was a folk remedy against intestinal worms and 'infusion of bear's foot' frequently killed the sick. Dr. Taylor remarks that "if persons are not always killed by such worm medicines, it must be a very fortunate circumstance." Worryingly, Burton's *Anatomy of Melancholy* [1621] advises us that it is a "sovereign plant to purge the veins of melancholy, and cheer the heart". Hopefully animals treated with it fared better. Parkinson, *in Theatrum botanicum* (1641), remarks that "a piece of the root being drawn through a hole made in the eare of a beast troubled with cough, or having taken any poisonous thing, cureth it." Gerard also relates that "old farriers used to cut a slit in the dewlap, and put in a bit of Beare-foot, and leave it there for daies."

The helleborine and helleborin glucosides present affect the heart similarly to digitalis (foxglove). The similar and related stinking hellebore *Helleborus foetidus* (*lower opposite*) is very similar in properties and toxicity.

23

Opium Poppy
Papaver somniferum

Family: *Papaveraceae*. Synonym: *Mawseed*. From Asia, but found on waste ground as a garden escape and grown as a crop in Britain. Grey and hairless, the flowers vary from white to purple in single and double forms. A deadly poison and class A drug. Manufacture or possession of opium is a serious offence. Poppy seed bread can produce a positive drug test.

The earliest images of this herb date from Sumeria, circa 4000 BC and it was used at Thebes in Ancient Egypt. The Greeks named it 'Mêkôn', the beloved youth of Demeter who transformed him into a poppy upon his death; indeed poppy seed cake was a sacrament in the rites of Demeter, and 'opos' was the white juice that dripped from the wand of Hypnos, god of sleep. In 1793 Woodville extolled its virtues in diarrhoea, cholera, syphilis, smallpox, asthma, epilepsy, gangrene and insomnia. He documented the development of tolerance in patients but seemed unaware of addiction, yet Britain and China went to war over opium addiction in the 1830s as the Chinese attempted to prevent the evils of British opium trading. By 1869 Britain was importing 127 tons annually to manufacture many different medicines. Laudanum was an alcoholic preparation and heroin, first synthesized in 1874, became the remedy of choice for asthma. Morphine is still vital in managing chronic pain and terminal care, and opiates remain the most effective treatment for dysentery.

Poppy seeds are valued as a food for pregnant women and mothers in Iran, India and Turkey, and in Lithuania, Slovakia and Hungary poppy seed dishes are eaten at Christmas. Lest we forget, *The Wizard of Oz*, de Quincey's *Confessions of an English Opium Eater*, Coleridge's *Kubla Khan* and the occult musings of Aleister Crowley were all inspired by the opium poppy.

25

LORDS AND LADIES
Arum maculatum

Family: *Araceae*   Synonyms: *Cuckoo pint, kings and queens, parson in the pulpit, wake Robin, starchwort, adder's root, bobbins.*   Flowering in woods, gardens and hedge bottoms from March to May, the bisexual flower (a striking upright 'spadix' within a sheath or 'spathe') is later transformed into a naked spike of orange berries.   Sometimes found among wild garlic—a member of the author's family was poisoned by this herb as a child, and children should be taught how to recognise it.

In Elizabethan times starch from the tuber was used to stiffen ruffs. 'Parson in the pulpit' alludes to the spathe and spadix, and 'cuckoo pint' from cuckold's pint refers to genitalia – the small 'pintle' or penis (spadix) appearing emasculated by the larger spathe. The spring 'cuckoo' is a frequent metaphor for cuckolding, and 'kings and queens' or 'lords and ladies' perhaps celebrates the union of male and female bringing fertility to both land and community, as expressed through the revelry surrounding May kings and queens. Robin Goodfellow is the wandering nature spirit of Ben Jonson's *Love Restored* [1612], carrying broom and candles to sweep away the winter's gloom. "A'wake Robin!"

The acrid and poisonous root prepared in the Isle of Portland was sold as 'Portland Sago'; a popular food among labourers that imparted strength and stamina. It was rendered edible by baking, drying and powdering, similar to the processing of the related Taro of the South Pacific. Used to cure ringworm, it was also a drastic purge and treatment for dropsy. Ingestion causes swelling of the tongue and internal inflammation that can result in death after several days of convulsive illness. Homeopathically, Arum is used to treat hot inflammatory conditions of the throat.

LILY OF THE VALLEY
Convallaria majalis

Family: *Ruscaceae*. Synonyms: *May lily, Our Lady's tears, ladder to heaven*. Found in dry woods, the leaves of this plant appear in ones and twos in early spring, and are followed by racemes of beautifully scented white bell-like flowers on nodding stems. The flowers develop into attractive scarlet berries. However, despite all appearances lily of the valley is a deadly poison, acting similarly to foxglove.

It was once held that this herb appeared where the tears of Mary fell to earth at the crucifixion. It was also supposed to have sprung from the blood of St. George (similarly St. Leonard in Sussex lore), when he was wounded whilst slaying the dragon. Another legend says that its fragrance will draw the nightingale to choose his mate in the depths of the wood.

Lily of the valley was once used by Russian peasants for heart problems; perhaps this herb was originally selected because of its heart shaped seeds. In modern medicine it is the source of a heart tonic and diuretic, with an action similar to digitalis though gentler. It slows the action of a weak and debilitated heart, and increases its power. Coles, in *Adam in Eden* [1657], describes the preparation of 'Aqua Aurea' or 'Gold Water' from the herb distilled in wine, and it was found to be so effective against apoplexy, or stroke that it was kept in vessels of precious metal. Culpepper wrote in his *Complete Herbal* [1653] that lily of the valley 'without doubt, strengthens the brain and renovates a weak memory'.

Lily of the valley used to be made into a soothing ointment for burns, and during the war in the trenches was used to make the antidote to poison gas. Symbolically too, this herb represents peace, happiness and harmony

29

FOXGLOVE
Digitalis purpurea

Family: *Scrophulaceae*. Synonyms: *Folks' glove, fairy thimbles, Devil's thimbles, Virgin's glove, dead man's thimbles, throatwort*. Found in woodland clearings and gardens, this tall downy biennial forms a rosette of basal leaves in the first year, the flower spike appearing from June onwards in the second. The well-loved flowers are tubular and pink, purple, or sometimes white, with dark spots inside reminiscent of an ulcerated throat – whence 'throatwort'. Most accidental poisonings result from it being mistaken for comfrey (with leaves untoothed). It can also be mistaken for elecampane or mullein. Foxglove is a deadly poison.

Culpepper recommended this plant for the 'King's Evil', and to cleanse old sores. The Anglo-Saxons called it *foxesglofa*, though some authors derive it from 'folk's glove', the glove of the fair folk. Dr. Withering, in *Account of the Foxglove* [1785], documented over 200 successful treatments, given mostly for heart failure. He was first instructed in its use by a village wise-woman – an event that changed medical history. At that time foxglove or 'throatwort' was also prescribed due to its appearance for throat infections. Although successful, the literature of the day reports commonplace poisonings derived from swallowing the medicine whilst gargling. Today, digitalis derived from foxglove is very important in the treatment of heart disease. Its action stimulates muscle, especially that of the heart, resulting in increased muscle tone, raised blood pressure, a strengthened pumping action and a lowered pulse. The drug is cumulative and overdose leads to toxicity – causing hallucination (coloured halos), very rapid pulse, low blood pressure, dizziness, vomiting and diarrhoea, collapse and death. Atropine (from deadly nightshade) is one of several antidotes usually given intravenously.

31

DOG'S MERCURY
Mercurialis perennis

Family: *Euphorbiaceae*. Synonyms: *Dog's cole*. A perennial indicator species of ancient woodlands, also found as a garden weed and under hedge bottoms. Usually under one foot tall carpeting in groups of same sex plants. Male plants bear small green flowers held above the leaves, and female plants bear relatively similar flowers on shorter stems. Similar and related to the poisonous 'annual mercury'. Causes severe poisoning which can result in death; in a recent incident the leaves were mistaken for peppermint. Symptoms include visual disturbance, vomiting, drowsiness, twitching and diarrhoea.

Mercury, the Roman messenger of the gods, presided over trade and led the souls of the newly dead to the underworld. Together with his Greek counterpart Hermes he was god of the crossroads, where herm posts were erected over much of Europe to act as shrines or omphali to the god, marking the intersection of the four directions with the cosmic axis.

Dog's mercury was once employed for jaundice and as a purgative. Culpepper recommended it for sore eyes and blocked or infected ears. The juice was used as a nasal douche for chronic catarrh and mixed with sugar or vinegar by country folk for removing warts. The plant yields an antiseptic and a fine blue dye which can be used as an indicator of pH. 'Mercurial' means 'changeable', and indeed the effects of mercury appear so; on the one hand it is sometimes described as a pot herb, yet on the other a dangerous poison. *Mercurialis annua*, the annual mercury is similar in appearance though slightly less poisonous, and is rendered safe to eat in some parts of Europe following lengthy boiling with frequent changes of the boiling water.

33

HEMLOCKS, COWBANE & DROPWORTS
to be avoided

Family: *Umbelliferae.* HEMLOCK: *Conium maculatum.* Synonyms: *Herb bennet, kecksies.* COWBANE: *Cicuta virosa.* Synonym: *Water hemlock.* HEMLOCK WATER DROPWORT: *Oenanthe crocata.* Synonyms: *Horse bane, dead tongue.* FINE-LEAVED WATER DROPWORT: *Oenanthe phellandrium.* Synonyms: *Horse bane, water fennel.* Hemlock (seeds illustrated above) is a tall spotted-stemmed biennial of hedge banks, woodland edges and stream sides. Cowbane and the water dropworts grow in wet places. People have mistaken them for root vegetables, celery and parsley.

In Anglo Saxon *hem–laec* means 'shore plant' which could equally refer to water hemlock or cowbane. Hemlock's purple spotted stem is said to bear the mark of Cain. The Greeks administered hemlock to Socrates and other alleged criminals, calling it *konas* meaning to 'whirl about'. Containing the poison coniine, it paralyses causing death by asphyxiation though peculiarly it leaves the mind clear. The juice of the stem smells mousy, and even sniffing it too hard is dangerous. Greek and Arab physicians applied it to tumours and painful joints, and archaeology reveals that Augustinian monks at Soutra in Scotland probably used it as a general anaesthetic in the twelfth century.

Cowbane (containing cicutoxin) and the various water dropworts are equally dangerous. Johnson tells us that in 1857 two farmer's boys tried cowbane and were found paralysed in the fields next to some chewed root. They soon expired. Hemlock water dropwort resembles wild celery in appearance and smell, and in 1856 seventeen hungry convicts in Woolwich ate it with disastrous consequences. The yellow juice was once used as a rat poison, but both water dropworts had a variety of other medical uses.

Hemlock

Cowbane

Hemlock water dropwort

Fine-leaved water dropwort

35

FOOL'S PARSLEY
Aethusa cynapium

Family: *Umbelliferae*. Synonyms: *Dog bane, dog's parsley, lesser hemlock*. A casual annual weed of cultivation and waste ground sometimes occurring in large bird-sown clusters. Short to medium in height, hairless and somewhat parsley like with white 'umbrella' flower heads appearing in June and July. Each group of flowers possesses long green bracts which hang below, making them look 'bearded'. Emits a characteristic mousy smell of hemlock when crushed. This plant can be mistaken for parsley, coriander or sweet cicely. The roots look like young turnips or radishes.

In Greek mythology, Aethusa was a daughter of Poseidon and Alycone. She bore a son to Apollo, called Eleuther. Accordingly, 'aethusa' became an epithet for a portico that was open to the sun, i.e Apollo.

Charles Johnson, in *British Poisonous Plants* [1856], recounts how in 1845 an unfortunate child mistook the bulbous roots for garden turnips and ate them. She was seized with abdominal pain and sickness, and suffered from lock-jaw, her death occurring soon afterwards. Another incident occurred in Germany and involved eating the leaves. Once again the patient's jaw was immobilised, and death soon followed. Poisoning with this plant results in pain, excitation, confusion, blurred vision and pupil dilation, with inflammation of the mouth and throat, duodenal congestion and skeletal paralysis; although the heart's action is unaffected. Historically this plant has been used to treat a range of problems affecting the digestive tract, for example (and rather worryingly) 'cholera infantum' – an often fatal form of childhood gastro-enteritis. It has also been used as a sedative. Of the diverse active ingredients, toxicity is thought to be due to the presence of polyines or polyacetylenes.

37

Autumn Crocus
Colchicum autumnale

Family: *Liliaceae*.   Synonyms: *Meadow saffron, naked ladies*. A grassland plant of lime soils. Unusually bearing white to purple flowers in autumn, but leaves and fruit the following spring. The leaves casually resemble wild garlic but they are deadly poisonous and have been gathered by mistake at the woodland's edge. Not related to the spice saffron, and not a true crocus at all.

Autumn crocus was named after the land of Colchis in Greek mythology, home to Medea the witch. Traditionally this plant signifies the spot where Jove and Juno lay together, and in another tradition it marks the place where Medea spilled the Promethean salve – usesd to make Jason invulnerable. The human race sprang forth from the clay suffused with this magical spillage.

The ancients likened the effects of *colchicum* to arsenic. The ancient Egyptians, Persians, Greeks and Romans all used it for rheumatism and gout, and, like us were conversant with its dangers. Theophrastus tells how slaves ate small pieces to make themselves too ill to work. Still a source of medicine for gout today, its usefulness is currently being evaluated as a treatment for cancer.

The whole plant contains the alkaloid colchicine, which prevents mitosis or cell division. Onset of gastric symptoms occurs 3 to 12 hours after ingestion. More serious complications follow on the second day as white blood cell production is inhibited, and the heart and vital organs are damaged. A painful death generally ensues over the course of several days.

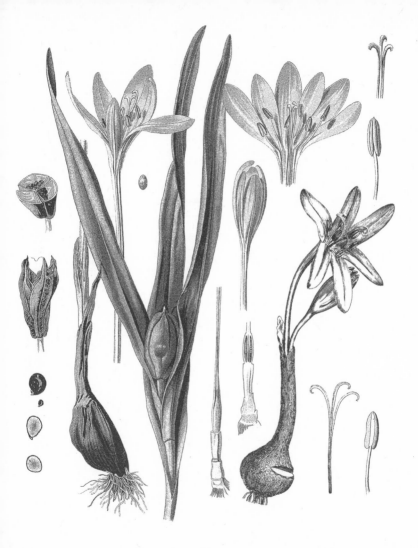

39

HERB PARIS
Paris quadrifolia

Family: *Melanthaceae.* Synonyms: *True love, true lover's knot, one berry.*
This low carpeting perennial of damp ancient woodlands prefers chalk
and limestone soils, growing to around one foot in height. Four leaves
are arranged symmetrically towards the top of a single stem that bears a
central greenish-yellow flower, later becoming a single plump blue-black
berry. Special care must be taken if this plant grows in your vicinity as
the berries are sometimes attractive to children and can prove fatal in
sufficient dose. The whole plant is an emetic and narcotic poison.

'Paris' means equal, and may refer to the attractive four-fold symmetry
of this plant. Alternatively, we are told in Homer's *Illiad* how Paris, Prince
of Troy abducted Helen from her husband Menelaus, precipitating the
Trojan War, after Aphrodite had led Helen to become obsessed with him.
Our herb certainly had a reputation as an aphrodisiac in former times!

Charles Johnson [1856] likens the effects of herb paris to the deadly
nightshade, whereas Mrs. Grieve [1931] likens it to opium poppy, and
recounts its use in Russia to treat 'madness'.

Paris is cooling, antispasmodic and sedative, and was traditionally used
to treat sore eyes, cramp, bronchitis, rheumatism and colic, and made into
an ointment for the treatment of gangrene, ulcers and tumours. The
active ingredient is a glucoside known as paradin. During the late 17th
and early 18th centuries, when mercuric chloride and arsenic were used
to treat syphilis, and arsenic was added to boiled sweets, herb paris came
to the rescue as antidote to both mercury and arsenic poisoning. It is
also the source of a fine yellow dye which can be fixed with alum.

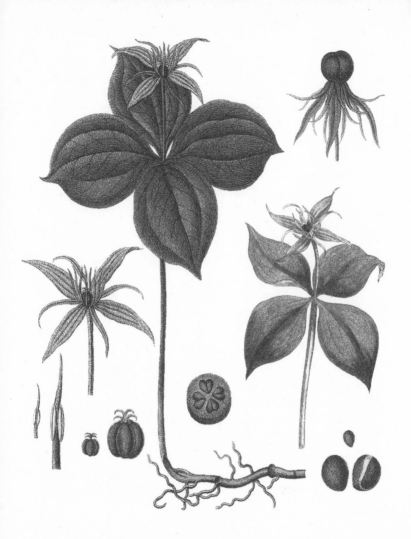

41

Mezereon and Spurge Laurel
Daphne mezereum & laureola

MEZEREON family (*illustrated*): *Thymelaeaceae*. A rare and beautiful native shrub. Popular in gardens for its fragrant clusters of early pink-purple blossoms, followed by the distinctive red fruit. All parts of this highly attractive plant are deadly poisonous.

Mrs. Grieve [1931] tells us that Russian peasants used a large dose as a drastic purge, although we are not told if this led to fatalities. Johnson relates that the berries have an influence over the nervous system somewhat resembling monkshood and deadly nightshade. Medicines prepared from bark, roots and berries were used to treat neuralgia, syphilis, rheumatism, snake bites, and by virtue of its ability to cause a flow of sebaceous fluid, certain skin diseases. Dr. Woodville [1791] relates that it was the first herb to compete with mercury in treating syphilis. He also relates the sad tale of a mother who gave it to her daughter, causing the child's death. In modern medicine it has found a place in treating leukaemia, and in homeopathy to treat eczma, shingles, respiratory and bladder complaints. Active ingredients include the resin 'mezeen', and a bitter glucoside known as 'daphnin'. The herb has been used in veterinary medicine to treat horses' hooves.

SPURGE LAUREL. *Daphne laureola* (*not illustrated*). Family: *Thymelaeaceae*. A small native evergreen shrub, preferring woodland on lime soils. Somewhere between a laurel and a large spurge in appearance, bearing small yellow-green flowers and shiny black fruit.

As for the above species, all parts of this plant are highly poisonous. Formerly used in treating intestinal parasites, but discontinued due to the high risk.

43

MISTLETOE AND YEW
Viscum album & Taxus baccata

MISTLETOE. Family: *Loranthaceae*. Synonyms: *Lignum Crucis, Herbe de la Croix*. Found on many trees but rare on oak. This is a poisonous festive decoration. In Norse myth Loki tricked Baldr's blind brother into killing him with a mistletoe spear. Mistletoe's habit resembles forked lightning and in Scandinavia epileptics carry mistletoe-handled knives to prevent them from being 'struck down' by their inner electrical storm. In Britain the oak was sacred to Taranis the thunder god and Pliny's *Natural History* recounts the Druids' ceremony of cutting mistletoe from an oak tree with a golden blade, accompanied by a white bull's sacrifice. Viscum album means 'white and sticky', and kissing beneath the sticky berries is an ancient custom that may celebrate the oak god's virility. 'Lignum Crucis' refers to the tradition that mistletoe was the wood of the cross. The leaf is a sedative nerve tonic and anti-convulsant used to treat epilepsy and hypertension, but the berries are more toxic. All parts can cause epileptic seizures in overdose.

YEW. Family: *Taxaceae*. Synonym: *Heben*. A 'conifer-like' evergreen, bearing red berries on female trees. All parts are poisonous, except the edible red flesh surrounding the seed. The hebenon of Shakespeare's *Hamlet* is often conflated with henbane. However, contemporary sources describe 'hebenon' as the bringer of stupor to those who abide in its shade, a property attributed to the yew. Yews have symbolic affinity with life and death, and can grow a new trunk from within a hollow one, or a circle of young trees from the extent of their roots. Some ancient yews may have originated from the sacred yew groves or *nemetiae* of the Druids but many churchyard yews were planted for making long-bows. Today, yew is the source of the chemotherapy drug Taxol used to treat some forms of cancer.

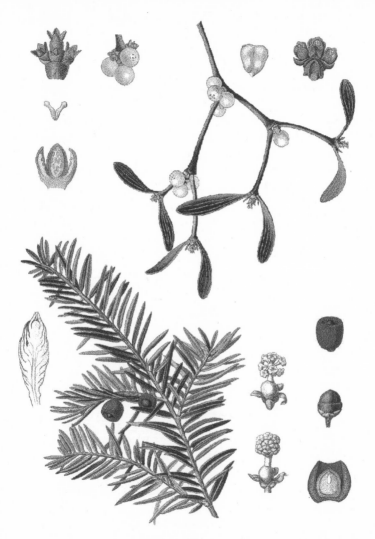

45

Frosted Fibre Cap & The Sickener
Inocybe maculata & Russula emetica

Frosted Fibre Cap. Family: *Cortinariaceae*. Found under beech trees on chalky soils. This chestnut brown mushroom with a slightly frosted appearance has a fibrous cap 2 to 8cm in diameter, with a central point or 'umbo'. The gills are grey-buff to cinnamon, and the ringless stem does not possess a 'volva' or death cup at the base. Many other inocybes possess a similar shape with mid-brown gills. Inocybes, such as this one and the related *Inocybe geophylla* (with a white cap) contain the alkaloid muscarine and can be deadly. Muscarine is also found in some clitocybe, mycena and amanita species.

When dried, this mushroom smells of musky perfume but do not be tempted to inhale as this can cause poisoning! Muscarine causes a slowed pulse, sweating, reduced pupil size, muscular twitching, discoordination and stomach cramps. It does not affect the brain directly, but causes confusional states due to its profound disturbance of the autonomic nervous system. The antidote is atropine derived from deadly nightshade, which reverses the neurotransmitter effects of muscarine.

The Sickener. Family: *Russulaceae*. Synonym: *Spit Devil*. Found in association with conifer trees. The similar beech wood sickener *Russula mairei* is found under beech. A small white stemmed mushroom with white gills, no ring or volva on the stem and a scarlet cap 3 to 10 cm across. This is one of a small number of the russula group that are actually poisonous. When eaten this mushroom causes gastric upset and vomiting although in healthy individuals the symptoms usually pass fairly quickly. The dried mushroom powder has allegedly been used as a seasoning in parts of Eastern Europe.

COMMON INK CAP & SATAN'S BOLETUS
Coprinus atramentarius & Boletus satanas

COMMON INK CAP. Family: *Coprinaceae*. Found in tufts associated with buried wood. This pale greyish-brown capped mushroom deliquesces as it ages, meaning that the edges of the cap gradually dissolve into a black ink-like substance which contains the spores necessary for the regeneration of the species. Do not consume alcohol within 24 – 48 hours of eating the common ink cap. This mushroom contains a very similar substance to the drug Antabuse that is used to treat alcoholism, and although tasty and edible, alcohol renders it poisonous, causing violent sickness and palpitations.

The 'ink' from this species was once collected by monks and boiled with cloves for use in writing. A similar species, the lawyer's wig or shaggy ink cap, *Coprinus comatus* is better recommended for eating because it does not cause a violent reaction when consumed with alcohol. It too deliquesces; the caps are removed from the stems and are good to eat before they turn inky, after which they are best suited to making a salty gentleman's relish or 'mushroom ketchup'.

SATAN'S BOLETUS. Family: *Boletaceae*. Found mostly under broad-leaved trees, this is an uncommon off-white capped relative of the edible porcini or penny bun mushroom, but unlike the penny bun (or cep) the sponge-like pores beneath the cap are red, and it has a red net-like pattern on the stem. This is one of the few mushrooms in the porcini group that are actually poisonous.

If eaten, Satan's boletus causes violent gastro-intestinal poisoning and can in some circumstances cause death. It is very dangerous indeed, so it is probably safest to avoid all red-pored boletes.

FLY AGARIC
Amanita muscaria

Family: *Amanitaceae*. Synonyms: *Magic mushroom*. Found in birch or coniferous woodland, the white spotted caps of vivid red or orange are delightful and evocative. The gills are white and the white stem possesses a ring and a volva or 'death cup' at the base. The mushroom of *Alice's Adventures in Wonderland* is potentially lethal, and when young it resembles a white 'egg' that can be mistaken for puffballs or field mushrooms.

Fly agaric assists Siberian shamen in their journey to the world of spirits, and in attaining supernatural prowess of movement and sight. In the Hindu Kush (Afghanistan), where it is known as 'Raven's bread', it is made into a beverage or massaged into the skin with henbane as an intoxicant. In tszarist Russia, fly agaric soaked in brine and vinegar was once popular, but its use was prohibited under communist rule. The Sami people of Northern Europe dry the caps and use them to attract the herds of reindeer, who love eating them. The reindeer's urine becomes psychoactive and is ritually consumed to aid with spirit walking, the animal's body having neutralised some of the toxic components. Across Eurasia it has been employed in folk medicine for sore throats, frost-bite, cancer and psychological ailments, often combined with other ingredients including rosebay willowherb, soured milk, and vinegar.

Fly agaric raises blood pressure and excites the central nervous system and is therefore dangerous. The documented effects (due to the presence of ibotenic acid and muscimol) are increased strength and visual acumen, nausea, twitching, exaggerated movements and the ability to leap high into the air. The effects are usually preceded by a period of deathly sleep, and overdose can cause death via collapse of the central nervous system.

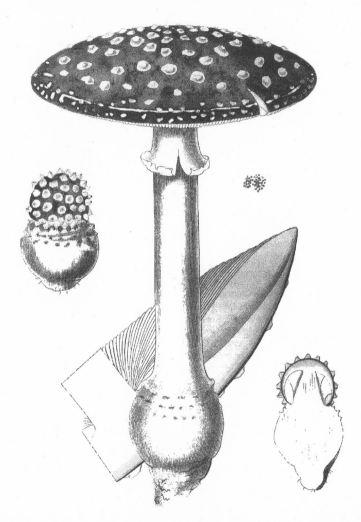

51

DEATH CAP AND PANTHER CAP
Amanita phalloides & Amanita pantherina

DEATH CAP. Family: *Amanitaceae*. Found in broad-leaved woodland from late summer to autumn. The cap varies from pale yellow to olive green and is 5 to 15 cm or 2 to 6 inches across with a stem 8 to 15 cm or 3 to 6 inches tall. The cap peels freely and has white gills. There is a ring on the upper stem, and a pronounced volva or 'death cup' at the base though this can be hidden by leaf litter. Young mushrooms emerge from a white 'egg'. Death cap is the most common cause of fatal mushroom poisoning and there is no antidote. It has been mistaken for the straw mushroom *Volvariella volvacea*, various green russulas, and puffballs and stinkhorns during the egg stage.

Toxicity, symptoms and poisoning are identical to the destroying angel (*see page 54*). Holy Roman Emperor Charles VI came to a mushy end by eating death caps, leading to the war of Austrian succession. In his *Mémoires* Voltaire wrote that "Ce plat de champignons a changé la destinée de l'Europe."

PANTHER CAP. Family: *Amanitaceae*. The panther cap, *Amanita pantherina*, is superficially similar to the fly agaric, although the cap is ochraceous brown, and it is found in both broad-leaved and coniferous woodlands from summer to autumn. However it is even more toxic containing very large amounts of muscimol and ibotenic acid, and when ingested affects the central nervous system, causing disorientation, hallucination and perceptual disturbance with exaggerated movement followed by coma and death if eaten in sufficient quantity. A number of deaths have resulted from the ingestion of this elegant mushroom.

53

DESTROYING ANGEL
Amanita virosa

Family: *Amanitaceae*. This pure white mushroom is found in mixed or broad-leaved woods from late summer to autumn. A similar deadly species *Amanita verna* is found in the spring. The cap is 5 to 12 cm or 2 to 4.5 inches across and peels freely. The stem is 8 to 15 cm or 3 to 6 inches tall with a lax ring and pronounced volva or 'death cup' at the base, although this may be hidden by leaf litter. The 'young' mushroom resembles a white 'egg', so beware of confusion with puffballs, stinkhorns, field and horse mushrooms, before the cap has opened to reveal its white gills. There is no antidote. Death follows in over 90% of cases and even with early medical intervention mortality is still distressingly high.

The deadly toxins present are divided into two groups; the amatoxins and the phallotoxins. Amatoxins are the cause of poisoning, because phallotoxins are not absorbed through the gut and do not enter the bloodstream. Amatoxins inhibit RNA production, resulting in cell death, and once transported to the liver they are recycled and re-absorbed over and over again causing incremental liver damage. Multi-organ failure follows if sufficient quantities have been ingested, and by the time symptoms occur much damage has already taken place.

Amatoxin poisoning is a notorious business, first noticed by extreme gastric upset 6 - 12 hours after ingestion. Gastric symptoms last for a day or more, and are followed by apparent complete recovery, but worse is to follow as organ failure takes place. At this stage, transplant surgery may be used in an attempt to save the patient's life. Death typically ensues 6 to 16 days after consumption.

Early intervention, preferably before the onset of symptoms, is vital.

APPENDIX I - TYPES OF POISON

PLANTS:

Due to the large and constantly growing number of toxic compounds that have been isolated from plants, it is most convenient to sort them by their chemical groupings. The main ones are:

ALKALOIDS – These are nitrogenous alkaline carbon compounds. They often make the plant taste bitter and are biologically very active, exhibiting a wide range of pharmacological effects depending upon the specific alkaloids present. Examples are; NICOTINE (tobacco), MORPHINE (opium poppies), ATROPINE (deadly nightshade), and CAFFEINE (coffee). Most alkaloids are considered toxic.

GLYCOSIDES – These organic compounds result from the combination of a sugar, such as glucose or fructose (known as the glycone), with another mollecule (known as the aglycone) via a glycosidic bond. Glycosides become active in the body when enzymes break the glycone-aglycone bond, releasing both concentrated sugars and the aglycone part to freely react within the biochemical systems of the body. An example is DIGOXIN (from foxglove) that has a powerful muscular and electrical effect upon the heart and is very toxic. AMYGDALIN is a glycoside found in many members of the rose family, for example the cherry laurel, and in many rose-family foods such as cherry, plum, peach, almond and apricot kernels, and apple pips. When acted upon by enzymes within the body, hydrogen cyanide is liberated from its aglycone and this can cause cyanide poisoning, however in the tiny quantities found in many foodstuffs it is more likely to behave as an anti-oxidant, which might be beneficial to health.

SAPONINS – These compounds cause a frothing effect when mixed with water, and they act as mild detergents. In fact, they are often the raw ingredients for vegetable soaps. Small quantities of saponins bind to cholesterol in the body, facilitating its excretion. However larger concentrations may damage cells and can be haemolytic (see haemolytic poisons below). Examples of plants considered toxic due to saponins include horse chestnut, and soapwort. Beneficial saponin containing foods include red peppers and chilli peppers, tomatoes and grape skins.

MUSHROOMS:

To date there has been far less research on the constituents of mushrooms compared to the vascular plants (above). Eating wild mushrooms is becoming very popular in the UK, and it is most useful to group the fungal toxins according to their physiological actions:

NEUROTOXINS – Many of these are alkaloids - see description above.

1. MUSCARINE poisoning (from *inocybes*, *clitocybes*, *mycenae* and others) affects the peripheral nervous system and is normally noticeable from 15 to 45 minutes after mushroom ingestion. It produces sweating, stomach cramps, increased urination and tear flow, lowered heart beat, blood pressure and respiration, and convulsions. In sufficient dose it occasionally leads to death by cardiac or respiratory failure, but poisoning usually subsides within 2 hours.

2. MUSCIMOL and IBOTENIC ACID are found in a number of mushrooms, typically the panther cap *Amanita pantherina* and fly agaric *Amanita*

muscaria. Symptoms typically occur around an hour after ingestion, and include twitching, euphoria, illusions, hallucinations, increased blood pressure and pulse, and hyperactivity interspersed with periods of deep sleep. Gastro-intestinal upset may also be present. Symptoms may last for up to 12 hours. Death from this type of poisoning is rare but it has occurred, and the panther cap is particularly dangerous.

3. PSILOCYBIN and PSILOCIN are found in numerous mushroom species, in particular among members of *paneolus, psilocybe* and *stropharia,* These neurotoxins act directly upon the brain and central nervous system producing profound feelings of excitation, euphoria, and hallucinations which can be either joyful or perplexing. Religious or spiritual experiences are frequently reported. Symptoms occur approximately 40 minutes after ingestion, and may last for 6 or more hours, after which time the patient normally makes a complete recovery. Rarely (and possibly owing to existing psychological issues) ingesting these toxins can lead to longer-term psychological illness.

PROTOPLASMIC POISONS

1. CYCLOPEPTIDES - These compounds vary in toxicity, and are even associated with a variety of beneficial medical effects where they occur in some families of green plants. However, they can be cytotoxic, immunosuppressive and are often enzyme inhibitors. Some of them are deadly poisons. The most deadly examples of these compounds are found among fungi, including the death-cap *Amanita phalloides,* destroying angel *Amanita virosa,* some *omphalotus, conocybe* and *galerina* species, and some small parasol species (*lepiota*). These deadly cyclopeptides (for example; amatoxin) halt cell replication and are recycled in the body rather than being broken down and excreted, leading to multiple organ failure and death over a period of days or weeks. Without very early medical intervention there is no known antidote. Symptoms of poisoning are initially violent gastro-intestinal disturbance, occurring at least 6 and usually 12 or more hours

after ingestion, followed by apparent recovery and then death from organ failure.

2. HYDRAZINES are alkaloids found in some species of false morels, gyromitra and verpa, that cause superficially similar symptoms to those of amatoxin poisoning from the death cap or destroying angel (*detailed above*). Though similar, poisoning is typically less severe.

3. ORELLANINE is found in *Cortinarius orellanus* and a number of other cortinarius species. Symptoms occur 2 - 3 days and up to 3 weeks after consumption, resulting in many cases of misdiagnosis. Initially symptoms are flu-like, but are followed by renal failure and may lead to death without further treatment.

GASTRO-INTESTINAL IRRITANTS - Fungi
may contain a wide variety of gastro-intestinal irritants of chemically different types, for example; the yellow-staining mushroom *Agaricus xanthodermus,* and Satan's boletus *Boletus satanas,* which both produce severe gastro-intestinal poisoning. Symptoms include violent stomach cramps, vomiting and diarrhoea 2 to 4 hours after ingestion, passing in 24 to 48 hours and rarely life threatening.

HAEMOLYTIC POISONS - Haemolytic
substances from various chemical groups cause the breaking open of read blood cells and the release of haemoglobin into the blood plasma, resulting in some cases in severe anaemia which can be very dangerous. An example of a good edible mushroom that contains a haemolytic poison is the blusher, *Amanita rubescens,* which is poisonous when raw but the toxicity is destroyed by heat. The mushroom is first parboiled (the water being discarded) and then cooked. Additionally, recent studies of the edible Jew's ear *Auricularia auricula-judae* show that it can significantly lower blood platelet count, particularly when eaten raw.

NOTE: *These lists are not exhaustive. Many more types of active substances are found in plants and fungi.*

Appendix II – Animals & Poisonous Plants

Plant	🐱	🐕	🐖	🐎	🐐
Buckthorn, Common / Alder / Purging*	☠	☠	☠	☠	☠
Apple (leaves, pips)*	?	☠	?	?	?
Autumn Crocus*	☠	☠	☠	☠	☠
Beech (nuts)*	?	?	☠	?	?
Bindweed*	?	?	☠	?	?
Black Bryony*	☠	☠	☠	☠	☠
Bluebell*	☠	☠	☠	☠	☠
Bog Asphodel*	?	?	☠	☠	☠
Box*	☠	☠	☠	☠	☠
Bracken* / Ferns in General*	☠	?	☠	?	?
Broom*	?	?	☠	?	?
Buttercup species* / Kingcup*	☠	☠	☠	?	?
Cherry, Wild / Bird / Domestic (leaves, pits)*	☠	☠	?	?	?
Clover, Alsike	?	☠	☠	☠	☠
Corn Cockle*	?	☠	☠	?	?
Cuckoo Pint*	☠	☠	☠	☠	☠
Daffodil*	☠	☠	☠	☠	☠
Darnel*	? ?	☠ ☠		?	?
Elder	☠	☠	?	?	?
Fool's Parsley* and Water Dropworts*	☠	☠	☠	☠	☠
Foxglove*	☠	☠	☠	☠	☠
Greater Celandine*	? ?	☠ ☠		?	?
Ground Ivy	?	☠	☠	?	?
Hellebores*	☠	☠	☠	☠	☠
Hemlock* and Water Hemlock (Cowbane)	☠	☠	☠	?	☠
Henbane*	☠	☠	☠	☠	☠
Holly*	☠	☠	☠	?	?
Honeysuckle*	?	☠	?	?	?
Horse Chestnut*	☠	☠	?	?	?
Horsetails*	?		☠	?	☠
Iris*	☠		☠	?	?

Plant	🐱	🐕	🐖	🐎	🐐
Larkspur*	☠	☠	☠	?	?
Lily of the Valley*	☠	☠	☠	?	?
Meadow Rue*	?	☠	?	?	?
Mezereon*	☠	☠	☠	☠	☠
Mistletoe*	☠	☠	?	?	?
Monkshood*	☠	☠	☠	☠	☠
Nettle (fine for humans after cooking)		☠			
Nightshade, Black / Woody / Deadly*	☠	☠	☠	☠	☠
Oak*	?	?	☠	?	?
Pasque Flower*	?	☠	?	?	?
Plum, Damson, Sloe (leaves, pits)*	?	?	?	?	?
Poppy, Corn / Horned / Opium*	☠	☠	☠	☠	☠
Privet*	☠	☠	☠	☠	☠
Ragwort*	?	☠	☠	?	☠
Rosebay & other Willow Herbs	?	☠	?	?	?
Sandwort*	?	?	☠	?	?
Snowdrop*	☠	?	?	?	?
Soapwort*	?	?	☠	?	?
Solomon's Seal*	?	☠	?	?	?
Sorrel	?	?	☠	?	?
Spindle*	☠	☠	?	?	?
Spurge Laurel*	☠	☠	☠	☠	☠
Spurge species*	?	?	☠	?	?
Squill*	?	?	?	?	?
St. John's Wort*	?	☠	☠	?	?
Thornapple	☠	☠	☠	☠	☠
Traveller's Joy*	☠	☠	?	?	?
White Bryony*	☠	☠	☠	☠	☠
Wild Garlic / Ramsons	?	?	☠	?	?
Vetch Species*	?	?	☠	?	?
Yew*	☠	☠	☠	☠	☠

☠ = *minor to major toxicity;*   ? = *toxic to some mammals;*   * *some toxicity to humans.*
Important: Omission of any plant is not an indication of safety.
This table focusses upon plants found in the wild – and strongly errs on the side of caution!